Daisy Learns About Strangers

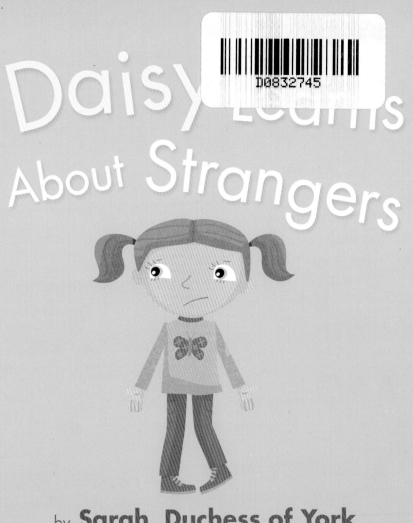

by **Sarah, Duchess of York**

Illustrated by Ian Cunliffe

Daisy Learns About Strangers

helping hand books

First published in Great Britain 2007 by Lloyds Pharmacy Ltd
Sapphire Court, Walsgrave Triangle, Coventry CV2 2TX
www.lloydspharmacy.com

In consultation with Cameron Wilson Ltd

Illustrated by Ian Cunliffe

'Ten Helpful Hints' contributed by Dr. Richard Woolfson,
child psychologist, Fellow of the British Psychological Society.

Printed in China

British Library Cataloguing in Publication Data
A catalogue record for this book is available from the British Library

ISBN 978-1-906260-05-7

All children face many new experiences as they grow up and helping them to understand and deal with each is one of the most demanding and rewarding things we do as parents. The helping hand books are for both children and parents to read, perhaps together. Each simple story describes a childhood experience and shows some of the ways in which to make it a positive one. I do hope these books encourage children and parents to talk about these sometimes difficult issues; talking together goes a long way to finding a solution.

Sarah, Duchess of York

Daisy was bored.
 She had been following her Mummy round the shops for what seemed like hours. And now Mummy had met a friend of hers and they were having a long talk about shopping, the weather and a television programme they had both seen the night before.

Just as she heard the word 'television', Daisy saw a television screen in another corner of the shop and it was showing a cartoon.

Daisy didn't recognise the cartoon, but it was much more interesting than listening to Mummy and her friend.

She walked towards the television.

As she walked closer, she could hear music and voices and soon she was completely lost in what she was watching and had forgotten all about her Mummy . . .

. . . who had not noticed that she had moved away.

"We always watch that game show," her Mummy was saying, "Daisy loves it, don't you Dai . . ."

Daisy was nowhere to be seen and her Mummy gripped her friend's arm in panic, looking frantically in every direction.

Meanwhile the cartoon had ended and Daisy suddenly realised where she was. Or rather where she wasn't.

She wasn't with her Mummy and, as she looked around at all the people walking past her, she felt very alone.

Then she remembered what she had been told to do if this happened and looked for someone in uniform.

There was a man near the front of the shop wearing a uniform with the word 'Security' on it. Daisy rushed up to him and said,

"Excuse me, but I've lost my Mummy. She was round by the carrots, but I must have walked off and now she's gone and I don't know if I'll ever see her again."

Daisy's lip began to tremble and she wanted to cry but was determined not to.

The security guard knelt down and said to Daisy,

"Don't worry, I'm sure she won't have gone very far. Tell me your name and we'll soon find her."

Soon there was an annoucement over the store loudspeaker:

"Will the mother of Daisy Johnson please come to the Manager's Office?"

Daisy's Mummy was in the Manager's Office before you could say Daisy Johnson!

"Why did you wander off, Daisy?" asked her Mummy, "you know you must stay with me when we are out shopping."

Daisy could see that her Mummy had been crying and now she couldn't stop herself either as she gave her Mummy the biggest hug.

The manager didn't like seeing Daisy cry so he sent his assistant off for a surprise for Daisy and a cup of tea for her Mummy.

"You did the right thing, Daisy, going to the security guard," said the manager to comfort Daisy who was still sniffing.

That night, Daisy's Mummy and Daddy explained that a stranger is someone you don't know. They also told Daisy that not all grown-ups are kind to children although at first they may seem to be.

"So it's important to remember a few simple rules, when you are out and about amongst grown-ups who you do not know,"
said her Daddy,

"I know, let's make up a rhyme so the rules are easy to remember."

They found a piece of paper and wrote:

Never take a stranger's sweet
Even if it's the biggest treat

Never take a stranger's hand
Touching by strangers is strictly banned

And never ever get into a stranger's car
Remember these rules wherever you are

The next day, Daisy showed her rhyme to Mrs Matthews, her form teacher, who asked Daisy to read it to the rest of the class.

When she had done so, Mrs Matthews told them about Kami, a boy who had been in her class some years before.

"At the end of the school day," she said, "all the class left as usual but, ten minutes later, Kami returned looking a little upset."

"Mrs Matthews," he had said, "there's a man at the gate who says he has come to collect me but I don't know who he is."

Mrs Matthews went with Kami to find the man and, after a few phone calls, it became clear that the man was someone who worked with his Daddy and who had offered to collect Kami that day.

Through a mix-up, no-one had told Kami and everyone agreed that he done absolutely the right thing by asking Mrs Matthews for help.

"So let's all say Daisy's rhyme one more time," said Mrs Matthews.

And they did.

Never take a stranger's sweet
Even if it's the biggest treat

Never take a stranger's hand
Touching by strangers is strictly banned

And never ever get into a stranger's car
Remember these rules wherever you are

TEN HELPFUL HINTS
FOR PARENTS WARNING THEIR CHILDREN
ABOUT STRANGERS by Dr. Richard Woolfson

1. Explain that appearances can be deceptive: your child can't always tell who is a "nasty stranger" just by looking at them, adding that they could appear friendly, generous and caring. Try to explain this carefully to avoid confusion, for instance so that she doesn't think all friendly people are actually dangerous.

2. Be clear but practical. For instance, there is no point in telling her "Don't talk to strangers when you are away from home," because that would be an impossibility. It would mean she shouldn't talk to shop assistants or to relatives who call round to see her friend when she happens to be playing there, and so on.

3. Make it absolutely clear though that she should never ever walk away with a stranger or out of a shop with them or go into a vehicle with them, no matter what that person says to them.

4. Present practical examples. Tell her, for example, "Don't take the hand of someone you do not know when you are in the street or in the park," "Never take a sweet from someone you don't know when you are not in our home," and "Never go into a car with a person you do not know." The more specific examples, the better.

5. Give these reminders regularly. Young children forget instructions from parents quickly so get into the habit of reminding your child about stranger danger each time she goes out, especially as her independence increases.

6. Let her ask as many questions as she wants. Her curiosity is endless and the whole concept of stranger danger is complicated. Allow her to ask any questions she wants about this without making her feel that she is being a nuisance.

7. Emphasise to your child that nobody has a right to touch her unless she is comfortable with that touch. She will understand that a cuddle or hug from you is perfectly acceptable but that it is not when it comes from someone she doesn't know (assuming you are not with her).

8. Tell her what to do if she gets lost. Suggest she asks for help from someone in a uniform, and if she doesn't know what a uniform is, show her pictures of, say, a policeman. If she is unable to see a person in a uniform, she should ask a woman for help (especially a woman with children) rather than a man.

9. Don't take anything for granted. She has lots of chances to be on her own in the shopping mall even when she is three or four – it only takes a second for her to slip out of your line of vision, for instance, she might absent-mindedly wander off while you chat to the shop assistant.

10. Tailor your comments to her age. If she asks "What will happen to me if I go with a stranger?", don't terrify her. Instead, give a basic explanation such as "A stranger might hurt you"; this provides a sufficient degree of warning without making the emotional impact of the message too extreme.

The helping hand books

Emily Moves Home
by The Duchess of York
Illustrated by Ian Cunliffe
A helping hand book from **Lloyds**pharmacy

Ben Goes to the Doctor's and Sophie visits the Dentist
by Sarah, Duchess of York
Illustrated by Ian Cunliffe
A helping hand book from **Lloyds**pharmacy

Simon Gets Better
by Sarah, Duchess of York
Illustrated by Ian Cunliffe
A helping hand book from **Lloyds**pharmacy

Holly's First Day at School
by Sarah, Duchess of York
Illustrated by Ian Cunliffe
A helping hand book from **Lloyds**pharmacy

When Katie's Mum and Dad Separated
by Sarah, Duchess of York
Illustrated by Ian Cunliffe
A helping hand book from **Lloyds**pharmacy

Daisy Learns About Strangers
by Sarah, Duchess of York
Illustrated by Ian Cunliffe
A helping hand book from **Lloyds**pharmacy

Harry Starts to Enjoy His Food
by Sarah, Duchess of York
Illustrated by Ian Cunliffe
A helping hand book from **Lloyds**pharmacy

Dalia Says Goodbye to Grandpa
by Sarah, Duchess of York
A helping hand book from **Lloyds**pharmacy

Jack Takes More Exercise
by Sarah, Duchess of York
Illustrated by Ian Cunliffe
A helping hand book from **Lloyds**pharmacy

Charlie and the Bullies
by Sarah, Duchess of York
Illustrated by Ian Cunliffe
A helping hand book from **Lloyds**pharmacy

Thomas and His New Baby Brother
by Sarah, Duchess of York
Illustrated by Ian Cunliffe
A helping hand book from **Lloyds**pharmacy

Sophie Makes Friends
by Sarah, Duchess of York
Illustrated by Ian Cunliffe
A helping hand book from **Lloyds**pharmacy

Lloydspharmacy